Postman Pat's Musical Special Delivery

Illustrations by Niall Harding

D0488674

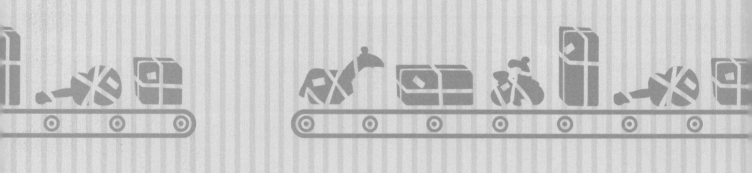

EGMONT

We bring stories to life

This edition published in 2013
by Dean, an imprint of Egmont UK Limited,
The Yellow Building, 1 Nicholas Road, London W11 4AN

Postman Pat® © 2013 Woodland Animations Ltd, a division of Classic Media UK Limited.
Licensed by Classic Media Distribution Limited.
Original writer John Cunliffe. Royal Mail and Post Office imagery is used by kind
permission of Royal Mail Group plc. All rights reserved.

ISBN 978 0 6035 6874 9
55631/1

Printed in Italy

All rights reserved. No part of this publication may be reproduced, stored in a retrieval system,
or transmitted, in any form or by any means, electronic, mechanical, photocopying, recording or
otherwise, without the prior permission of the publisher and copyright owner.

There's a concert at the school, and Postman Pat must get a musical special delivery there on time. Can Postman Pat show that the Special Delivery Service always gets through?

The Special Delivery Service van was being cleaned at Ted's car wash. Bubbles were everywhere! Suddenly, Postman Pat's phone rang its special ring.

"Special Delivery Service, Postman Pat speaking," he answered.

It was Ben, at the mail centre.

"Pat, I've got an urgent special delivery for you," said Ben. "It's over at Pencaster Station with Ajay."

Postman Pat arrived at Pencaster Station and found Ajay playing a piano.

Just then, Postman Pat's phone rang again. It was Ben. He said that the piano had to be delivered to the school in time for Lizzy to play her first piano solo in a concert.

Ajay helped Postman Pat push the piano into the van.

"Come on, Jess," said Pat. "Lizzy is waiting for us."

At the school, the children were excited about the concert and were making lots of noise with their instruments! Julian played the drums and Bill played a guitar. Lizzy practised on an electric keyboard.

"Good news, Lizzy," said Lauren. "The piano is on its way. You'll have plenty of time to rehearse before the concert starts."

As Postman Pat and Jess raced to the school, some cows wandered into the middle of the road! Pat braked, and the van screeched to a halt. He jumped out of the van. Stopping so quickly had made one of the van's tyres go flat.

"It's a puncture Jess, we need help," said Postman Pat.

He called Ted at the garage.

Ted soon arrived. But he hadn't brought the tool he needed to change the tyre. So they decided to drive the piano to the school in Ted's van. Ted went to get the piano out of Postman Pat's van.

"Nice and steady, Ted," said Postman Pat. "Not too fast."

Suddenly the piano slid out of the van, with Ted on top of it!

"Whooah!" called out Ted. "Oh dear!"

Postman Pat and Jess jumped out of the way as Ted and the piano rolled past them. It smashed through a gate, with Ted still holding on tightly!

"Oh! Who'd have thought a piano could go so fast!" shouted Ted.

At last the piano slowed down and stopped in the middle of a muddy field. Ted climbed safely down – but then he fell backwards into a dirty puddle!

"Are you all right, Ted?" asked Postman Pat. "We need to get this piano into your truck."

"It's too muddy, Pat," said Ted. "We'll never push it out of this field."

Just then, Jess meowed and leapt on to a trolley on the nearby train track.

"The trolley!" laughed Pat. "Jess, you clever cat. This disused track goes to Greendale. We could use the trolley to get us there."

Back at the school, Lizzy was upset that the piano had not arrived yet.

"I don't want to play in the concert any more," said Lizzy quietly. "I'm not going to have enough time to practise, it will be awful."

Bill tried to make her feel better.

"There's still time, Lizzy!" said Bill. "Let's go outside and see if we can see Pat coming."

Postman Pat and Ted carefully strapped the piano on to the trolley. Then they took turns to push down on the trolley's lever. They started to move slowly along the track.

"Heave ho, heave ho!" Postman Pat and Ted called out, as they pushed the lever.

"Faster Ted, I've got to get this special delivery to the school, or the show can't go on!" puffed Postman Pat.

At last, the trolley and the piano arrived at Greendale Station. Postman Pat and Ted huffed and puffed as they took the piano off the trolley.

Just then, Pumpkin clip-clopped past with Amy. Pat had a great idea. Amy carefully tied a harness around Pumpkin so he could pull the piano along behind him!

"Come on Pumpkin, that's it," said Amy. "One piano on its way!"

Lizzy was waiting outside the school with her friends. At last they spotted Postman Pat with the piano.

"I haven't had time to practise," said Lizzy sadly. "What if I make a mistake?"

"No one will mind if you make a mistake, Lizzy," said Postman Pat, kindly.

"Everyone just wants to hear you play!" cheered on Meera.

At last, inside the school, the concert began. Lizzy played a wonderful tune on the piano!

The audience clapped, and everyone shouted "Hooray!"

"Thanks, Pat," said Lizzy.

"You're welcome," said Postman Pat. "The Special Delivery Service always gets through. Mission accomplished!"

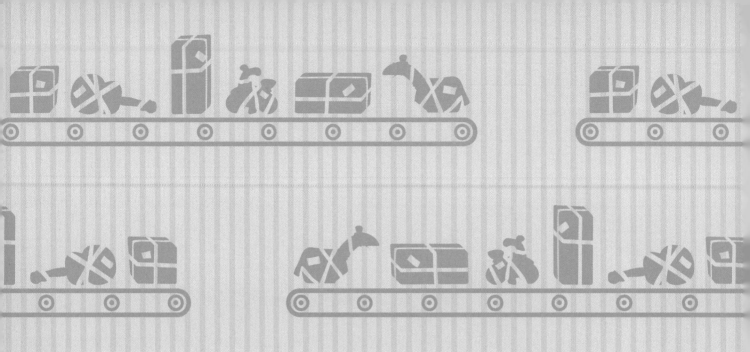

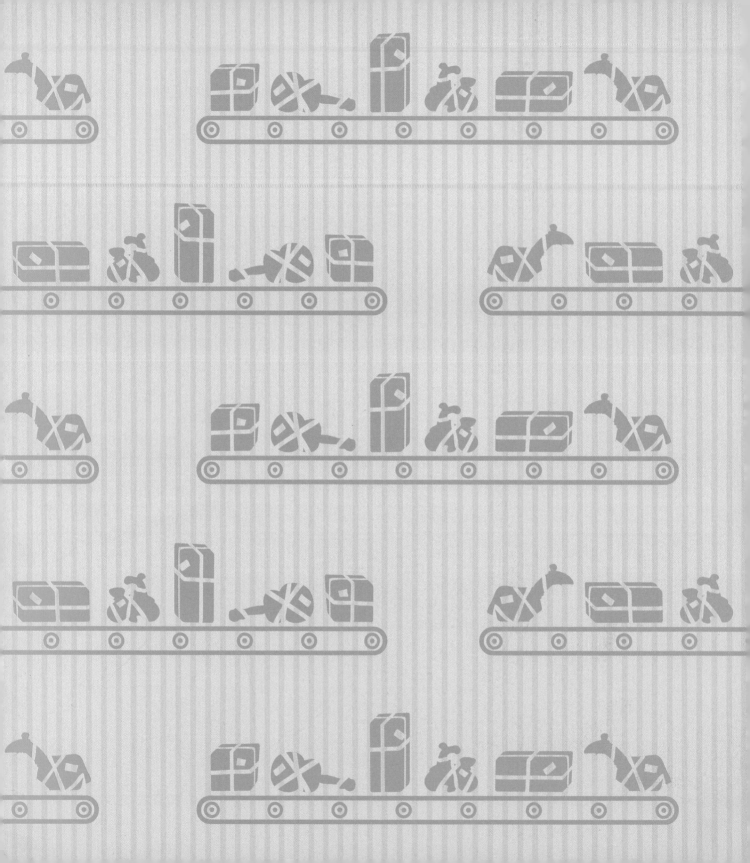